Grace the Pirate

JAMES RIORDAN

Illustrated by Steve Hutton

Oxford University Press 1996

Oxford University Press, Walton Street, Oxford OX2 6DP

Oxford New York
Athens Auckland Bangkok Bogota Bombay
Buenos Aires Calcutta Cape Town Dar es Salaam
Delhi Florence Hong Kong Istanbul Karachi
Kuala Lumpur Madras Madrid Melbourne
Mexico City Nairobi Paris Singapore
Taipei Tokyo Toronto

and associated companies in
Berlin Ibadan

Oxford is a trade mark of Oxford University Press

© James Riordan 1996
First published 1996

ISBN 0 19 916925 X   School edition
ISBN 0 19 918526 3   Bookshop edition

Printed in Great Britain by Ebenezer Baylis

Illustrations by Steve Hutton

For Tania and Marie

CHAPTER 1

From the diary of Mungo Watkins

I wouldn't say I was a wicked man. But I'll tell you no lie, mateys. I've sailed with a good many pirates: some bad, some mad. Some would slit your throat as soon as look at you.

All the great pirate captains had one thing in common. They were scared of nothing, not even death.

They could lead a gang of the toughest, meanest villains on God's earth – against the biggest ships and the strongest forts. Even against entire cities.

They didn't all start out as pirates. Some fell into pirate hands and had no choice. Either they walked the plank or served under the skull and crossbones.

There were women too; and some were as tough as any man. All the same, it was a pirate rule that:

But some did of course. Sometimes they chose to; sometimes they became pirates by chance. My story is about one such lass: young Grace Barry.

It all started early one morning when our ship, the *Sea Devil*, lay at anchor. Our Captain Cutthroat spotted a merchant ship sailing into the bay.

CHAPTER 2

A girl on board!

'Ah-ha,' cried Cutthroat. 'What luck! There's more crew for us. D'you think they'd like to join us, lads?'

He grinned cruelly, adding, 'We'll take the fit and toss the rest overboard.'

We showed our guns and, in no time at all, the new ship had given up without a fight.

Bert Bunce, the bosun, brought some of the sailors before the captain. All had to serve on board our pirate ship.

'Name? Age? Job?'

'Adam Goss... 18... ship's carpenter.'

'Aye.'

'Jonah Feltham... 32... gunner.'

'Aye. Next.'

'Rob Birdson... 27... ship's cook.'

'Aye. Look lively!'

'Grace Barry... 15...'

'Aye – ai-yai-yai!'

'Hold hard!' yelled Captain Cutthroat. 'What's that last one?'

'Grace Barry.'

'But that's a girl's name!'

'I *am* a girl.'

'You can't be. This is a pirate ship. We don't allow girls on board. Death! That's for bringing girls on my ship!'

'Well, I *am* a girl. And since *you* brought me on board, death to *you*!'

Cutthroat was lost for words. He swore into his black beard and at Bert Bunce.

'You stupid codfish! Can't you tell a girl from a boy? She's Grace – dis-Grace more like it! Now what are we going to do?'

We all muttered among ourselves. Rules were rules, after all.

Grace watched calmly as we all argued. Some were for tossing her overboard. I was against it. It didn't seem right to kill the poor girl. It wasn't her fault she was on a pirate ship.

But Captain Cutthroat was set on getting rid of her. He couldn't forgive her for making him look a fool. Finally, we decided to put her ashore at the first island we came to.

Grace was taken down below, while the captain shouted orders. 'Open up the stolen rum, shipmates.'

CHAPTER 3

The storm

That night a storm blew up. Waves reared their foaming heads, blinding rain poured down. The boat rolled and heaved.

I don't recall much about that night. I do remember seeing the watchman snoring in a pool of rum. And no one was at the wheel. I don't suppose any of us could stand, let alone steer. We might well have sunk to a watery grave had not someone taken charge.

The sailor began to shout orders.

'Trim the mainsail! More tack on the jib! Look lively!'

The slim figure in baggy breeches and calico shirt saw that we were all too drunk or scared to free the topsail. So the young sailor scrambled up to the top of the mast.

There, swaying in the gale, he cut free the tangled sail. All the while, the ship pitched and tossed in the towering seas.

Once back on deck, the sailor grabbed the wheel which was swinging this way and that in the heavy seas. And he steered the ship safely through the waves. Whoever he was, he was a born sailor.

It was a calm, grey morning when we finally staggered on deck. Quite a few of us were sick and holding our aching heads.

'Where's the bold sailor who saved us?' I called.

He was nowhere to be seen.

'What a rum do!' cried the bosun. 'Perhaps it was a ghost...'

'More likely one of the new hands,' I replied.

Yet no one came forward.

Just then a shout came from the lookout up in the crow's nest:

'Land ahoy! Land ahoy!'

In the distance we could dimly make out a green island and sandy bay. Just the spot for unwanted girl pirates.

'Right, girl,' yelled Cutthroat above the wind, 'when we reach the bay you'll swim for it – see who makes land first, you or the sharks!'

He gave a cruel laugh.

As the ship sailed in close to the bay, a couple of us sailors went to toss Grace overboard. But she pushed us away, shouting to the crew, 'Is none of you man enough to stick up for me?'

Now, though we were scared of Cutthroat, we weren't all cowards. I couldn't help myself.

'If we chuck her into the water,' I said, 'the sharks'll get her. Even if she makes land, she'll starve to death. Let's leave her be. We could drop her at the next port.'

Cutthroat would have none of it. But Grace was not going to give in without a fight.

'Where was your captain last night? Dead drunk!' she cried. 'You could have all been drowned, for all he cared.' She gave me a grateful look. 'Why don't you listen to the mate?'

At that Cutthroat snatched his cutlass out of his belt.

'That girl goes into the water. Any man who disobeys me will taste my steel!' he roared. 'You first, Mister Watkins!'

I bit my tongue.

With Grace wriggling like an eel, it took half a dozen sailors to bundle her over the side. She hit the sea like a sack of herring tails. Some of the crew laughed and jeered as they watched the race for shore. Grace was swimming a leg's length ahead of the sharks.

But not all of us were laughing.

Some of us were deeply ashamed.

All at once, it came to me. I knew I'd seen those baggy breeches before! Of course, it was the bold sailor from the previous night.

That was Grace!

'Come on, missy, you can do it!' I whispered, willing her to escape the sharks.

And she did. She just made land as a shark's jaws snapped shut on her sandal.

I watched her crawl up the sand and sit there, gazing after our ship as we sailed over the horizon. Her shouts came to us on the wind.

'I'll show you! You'll live to remember Grace Barry!'

CHAPTER 4

The desert island

Ah, she was a one, that Grace! Who else would have the courage and sense to stay alive on a desert island? Years later, she told me about it. This is her story, if I remember rightly.

She was almost done for when she crawled up the beach, half drowned, scared and very angry. She lay there for a couple of hours. But it was never her way to stay down for long. She staggered to her feet and started to explore.

Straight away she saw that there were banana, coconut and date palms. Now, at least, she had food.

Shaking off her tiredness, she shinned up a coconut palm, and shook down some nuts.

She then broke off several broad green leaves, each bigger than herself. Soon she had also piled up dates and yellow-green bananas.

'At least I won't starve to death,' she told herself.

But besides food she needed somewhere safe to sleep. She picked a spot on the beach, in the open; there she could keep an eye out for passing ships.

First she combed the beach for wood. Soon she made a big pile of broken branches, seaweed and grasses – there was even an old sun-bleached oar.

The dried seaweed and grasses covered her floor. She used wood for the walls, slanted like a tent. Then she tied banana leaves over the cracks with coconut fibre.

'It may not be a palace,' she sighed, 'but it'll do. At least it'll save me from the worst of the rain, wind and sun.'

The sun was hanging low over the sea. She was stiff and sore – and very hungry. First she ate some dates and bananas, and then she split open a coconut on a stone to drink the sweet milk.

At last, she lay down upon the grass floor in her new house and watched sea-fleas jumping up and down on her new mattress.

'I've got through one day,' she told herself. 'Tomorrow, I'll explore the whole island. Who knows? Maybe I'll find some company.'

Little did she know she already had some!

Someone was watching her even as she fell asleep.

She must have slept for many hours, for when she awoke, the sun was already high in the sky. What was that noise outside?

Suddenly, she heard it again. Someone was moving about outside the hut. They were creeping up on her – no doubt to slit her throat!

Grabbing her only sandal, she sat up, her heart in her mouth.

All at once, an ugly bearded figure
poked its head through the doorway…

She didn't scream. Instead, she
giggled with relief and the bearded
figure scuttled away, tail between its
legs.

'A fine pirate you'd make, Billy Goat,'
she cried. 'Fancy running away at the
sight of a girl!'

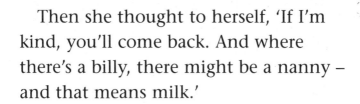

Then she thought to herself, 'If I'm kind, you'll come back. And where there's a billy, there might be a nanny – and that means milk.'

She sat down on the warm sand and cupped her chin in her hands, gazing out to sea.

'If only I could catch some fish,' she thought. 'But I need a fire to cook them on.'

All of a sudden she had an idea.

'What if I gather some dry leaves and wood bark? I can use this bit of broken glass to focus the sun's rays on the leaves.'

It was worth a try. After collecting some leaves and placing the broken glass between the midday sun and the dry leaves, she sat patiently waiting. Several minutes later, blue-grey smoke began to drift upwards.

This was followed by a sudden burst of flame. Quickly adding more twigs, she soon had a good fire blazing on the sand.

'Now all I need is a fishing line,' she thought. 'I know… What if I twist my earrings into fish hooks? Then I can tie them to string twisted from palm fibre. And I'll stick a bit of crab on the hook as bait. There's my fishing line!'

An hour or so later she was standing on a rock above the sea. Her fishing line was dangling into clear blue water where no one had ever fished before. And in next to no time she had a pile of flapping, shining fish at her feet.

She tossed the tiddlers back, took half a dozen big fish and pushed a stick through each one. Then she strung them across her barbecue.

A delicious smell of grilled fish floated across the sand and into the trees. While she was busy eating, out of the corner of her eye she noticed something moving. There were two shadowy figures among the palm trees.

'Aha,' she said to herself. 'Welcome to dinner, Bill and Nan. If you want food, come and get it.'

She cut up a few bits of date and coconut and left them on the sand next to her.

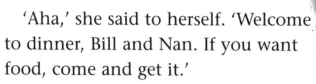

Slowly but surely, the goats came to eat out of her hand. After that, they visited her every day for scraps to eat. Within a week, the nanny goat let Grace milk her into a bowl made from half a coconut shell.

So now she had a regular supply of goat's milk. She also had all the fruit and coconuts she could eat, not to mention her fishing catch. Sometimes it was a fat eel, sometimes a spiky crab or lobster, even pretty rainbow fish.

One dark night, the skies opened and the rains came down.

By now she had made her home very strong; so it stood up to the storm. Next morning, when she looked at her raintraps, there was a good supply of fresh water.

She seemed to have all she needed.
But even with her two goats, she was
lonely. Not once had she spotted a
passing sail. What if she had to spend
the next twenty-five years on the
island, like Robinson Crusoe? Or even
the rest of her life?

It did not bear thinking about.

CHAPTER 5

The skeleton

But she was not the first on the island.

One day she made a grim discovery. It was while she was exploring a new part of the island. Stepping into a clearing, she saw something which made her stand still in horror.

There lay a skeleton. It was stretched out beneath a fig tree – for all the world as if it was fast asleep.

As she came near, she noticed a small wooden box clutched in its right hand. The forefinger of its left hand was pointing to the grassy bank opposite.

With a shudder, she pulled the box from the fingerbones and opened it up. Inside she found a piece of paper with faded writing on it.

My name is Ben Budd, I was marooned by pirates in 1673. Bury My Bones and take my treasure. It's no use where I'm going.

She glanced round, following the line from finger to bank. Then she prodded the soil with a stick until she struck something hard.

Brushing away the loose earth, she eased a wooden chest from its grave. The metal clasp had long since rusted away, so it was easy to force open the lid. Her heart beat faster with excitement. Yet nothing could have prepared her for what was inside the chest.

The sight was dazzling. Rubies and pearls gleamed amidst glittering piles of gold coins.

She put both arms up to her elbows into the treasure, feeling the cold hard coins. Then she let the rubies and pearls trickle through her fingers like running water.

'Poor Ben's right,' she said slowly. 'It's no use to him now. The least I can do is bury his bones.'

As best she could, she dug a grave for the dead man's remains. Partly with her foot, partly with a stick, she pushed the bones down into the hole. But imagine her horror when the skull came apart from the body. It rolled slowly down the slope...

She had to coax it into the grave with a stick!

Next she made a little wooden cross which she stuck into the ground above the skull. A few days later she wrote the words 'BEN BUDD 1673' on the cross with a burning stick. For the moment, however, she stood there in silence.

She was thinking of Ben's lonely fate. Was this what awaited her?

CHAPTER 6

Rescued

One of her first tasks on the island was to keep count of the passing days. Each palm tree along the shore was a week. So with a sharp shell she made seven cuts in its bark for each day of the week.

She was already on her thirty-third tree.

Then, one morning, she spotted the dim shape of a ship sailing through the mist.

At long last! Hooray! Her heart leapt.

Just as quickly it sank down to her feet. For there was the skull and crossbones fluttering from the ship's mast.

It was the hated *Sea Devil*, the cause of all her troubles!

Were the pirates returning to make sure she was dead? Maybe Cutthroat could not risk her giving evidence against him. There was nowhere to hide.

She stood, waiting for the worst...

Can you think how she must have felt? Poor Grace!

But we weren't feeling too good in the *Sea Devil* either, I can tell you. We'd been sailing about lost for days. Cutthroat had gone, you see, and none of us could work out our course. Suddenly I saw the island – and it looked sort of familiar. One of the lads cried, 'That's it! That's where our bad luck began.'

And we knew we'd come back to where Cutthroat had thrown Grace overboard.

Was she still alive?

Our ship dropped anchor off shore. I sat in a longboat with two other pirates and headed for land. When we reached the island I stepped forward to greet Grace. I could see the poor girl thought we had come to kill her.

'Ah, Miss Grace,' I said with a
nervous smile. 'How glad we are to find
you alive. The men sent me for you.
You see, my dear, we know it was you
who saved us from the storm.'

I could see the surprise on her face.
But she still didn't trust me. So I told
her the whole story.

'We've had an 'orrible time of it. After
we left you we drank away all our
booty. Then we got caught by the Navy.

'That evil Cutthroat went and ratted on us just to save his own skin, rot him. We were lucky not to hang. We escaped but we're lost and most of the crew's sick. And we're having to drink stinking water and eat maggoty meat and biscuits.'

She stared hard at me.

'Well, what do you want of me?' she asked.

'We... er... need a good captain – or we're done for,' I mumbled. 'You're our only hope.'

Grace smiled to herself.

'We'll see about that,' was all she said.

Turning to her goats, she said, 'Well, shipmates, what do you say? Shall I take charge of these men? Or shall we let them stew in their own juice?'

One goat nodded wisely and waggled his beard.

The other just stared at my red whiskers; she was no doubt wondering whether they were good enough to eat.

'All right,' Grace said at last, 'I'll join you. But you'll do as I say. Have your men carry my chest on board.'

Turning away, she bid goodbye to her goats and, silently, to the ghost of poor old Ben Budd. Then she stepped quickly into the longboat.

Once on board, Grace called all of us together. What a sorry sight we must have been! Some were too weak to stand; they had to lean on each other for support. In a calm, firm voice Grace spoke from the bridge.

'I agree to be your captain. But... there'll be changes made. Call yourself pirates? Why, you're just a pack of cowards. When you've food and rum in your bellies, you can toss a girl to the sharks – and laugh about it. But would any of you survive a week on a desert island?'

Most of the men shuffled their feet nervously.

'Now, listen to what I say,' continued Grace. 'Take it or leave it. Since I'm captain, I re-name this ship *She Devil*. Haul down the Jolly Roger and run up the Jolly Jane. We'll have a woman on a red flag instead of that skull and crossbones. That'll show who's boss.

'Next, we'll rob only rich ships from the Spanish Main. And we'll give half our booty to the poor along the coast. The rest we'll divide up fairly among the crew. For a start, we'll all take equal shares of my treasure chest!'

There was a hush for a full minute.
Then the men started muttering among
themselves. After a while, we all fell
silent. Then, we let out a roar in chorus.
'Aye-aye, Captain Grace!'

Grace grinned from ear to ear.
'Now, you cowardly cutthroats,' she
yelled, 'bring me my tea and biscuits
and let's get underway.'
So began Grace's new life as pirate
captain.

CHAPTER 7

Treasure

Grace had no time to get used to her new job. Almost at once we spotted a white sail in the distance. She was a large ship, about four hundred tons, and she was clearly carrying a heavy cargo.

Along her sides were twenty cannons. For sure her captain would use them to blow our little ship out of the water. He had spotted us and was now heading towards the *She Devil*.

A buzz of excitement rose from end to end of our ship.

Grace had no choice. She would have to stand and fight – or die with the rest of us.

'Right, men, to your posts,' she shouted. 'We'll attack from the stern so as to avoid their guns.'

Calling to the chief gunner, she added, 'Mister Feltham, keep your powder dry. When we get close, shoot her sails down. That way, she can't make a run for it.'

To a couple of young sailors, she said, 'Tom, Billy, when I give the word, I want you to jump overboard. Swim to her rudder and jam it hard so she can't turn about and run us down.'

To the rest of us, she cried, 'Follow me over the rail as we draw alongside. Our main weapons are speed and surprise. If we wait we'll be blown to bits!'

If the ship was aware of our plans, she didn't show it. In any case, there was little she could do. She was too heavy to turn quickly to meet our attack. Such was the speed of our move that her sailors were taken completely by surprise.

By the time the alarm went up, their sails were tumbling about their heads. And we were swarming over the ship's sides, with Grace in the lead.

Like the rest of us, she tried to make herself look as fierce as possible. In her right hand she held a long pistol; in her left she waved a sharp knife – though I'm sure she would rather have died herself than use either!

A white handkerchief gathered up her long fair hair – so no one could tell she was a girl.

Luckily, the captain gave in without a fight. He handed over his cargo in exchange for safe passage and no blood spilled.

We took as much as our small ship could hold: silks and jewels, gold and silver, spices and tobacco. But Grace told us, 'Take some medicine, plenty of candles and rope, and as much bread and meat as we can carry.'

Once back on board, Grace shouted,
'Let's get out of here!'

And not a moment too soon. For the
ship had turned at last and was firing
her cannons at us. One cannon ball
bounced off the water and tore through
the *She Devil*'s sails.

But it did little damage thanks to
Grace's swift action.

All the same, it was a narrow squeak.

We had rich pickings. What with
Grace's treasure as well, we could all
now retire in comfort. But most of us
had the sea in our blood and didn't
fancy life on land. And few of us
wanted to leave our captain. She had
brought us good luck.

Shortly after, Grace had the offer of
carrying cargo along the American
coast. So she put it to us.

'Well, you black-hearted villains, shall
I make honest men out of you?'

We talked it over among ourselves. It didn't take long. I stepped forward with the men's reply.

'Captain Grace, even if it means going straight,' I said, 'the men say they'll follow you anywhere.'

And we did.

The *She Devil* soon became the best trading ship on the high seas. Even the most bloodthirsty pirate steered well clear of us. It was bad luck to attack a ship captained by a woman.

In any case, they had too much respect for Grace the Pirate.

Historical note

Pirates have been around a long time. There are still a few on the high seas today. But the Golden Age of Piracy was between the 1660s and 1770s. The favourite hunting ground was the Caribbean and the American coast between Florida and North Carolina.

That was mainly because ships had to sail through the Caribbean, taking treasure from South America back to Europe. Rich pickings for pirates.

Pirate life was usually short and anything but sweet. The punishment for piracy was death. As a rule, pirates were hung in chains with their toes above the low water mark. They were then left until 'three tides had washed over them.'

We do not hear much of women pirates. There may not have been many of them, but such pirates as Grace O'Malley, Anne Bonny and Mary Read – and others down the ages – were as brave and daring real figures as any male pirate.

No pirate chief, man or woman, can match Ireland's Grace O'Malley: for over fifty years in the 16th century she pirated from Ireland to Spain.

Anne Bonny and Mary Read were two remarkable women who sailed together in the early 18th century.

At first, they pretended to be men;
yet once they had won respect for being
as tough and fearless as any man, they
went about openly as women.

The two women sailed as pirates for
four years before being caught – while
Mary died in prison, Anne was set free,
married and never returned to sea
again.

About the author

I was born by the sea in Portsmouth a fairly long time ago. As a boy, I heard many tales of mutinies, pirates and press gangs; of bold and fearless men. And I wrote many stories for children about brave heroes.

One day, my daughter Tania and her daughter Marie asked me why all pirates were men; didn't women go to sea? And as I dug into the past, I discovered quite a few women – authors had somehow written them out of history. That is how Grace came to have her story told.

Other Treetops books at this level include:

Danny's Secret Fox by Susan Gates
The Night of the Ticklers by Paul Shipton
Petey by Paul Shipton
Climbing in the Dark by Nick Warburton
Okay, Spanner, You Win! by David Clayton

Also available in packs
Stage 14 pack B	0 19 916926 8
Stage 14 class pack B	0 19 916927 6